Published by MQ Publications Limited
12 The Ivories, 6–8 Northampton Street, London N1 2HY
Tel: 020 7359 2244 / Fax: 020 7359 1616
email: mail@mqpublications.com

ISBN: 1-84072-515-X

1 3 5 7 9 0 8 6 4 2

Printed and bound in China

you make me Happy

and other things I love about you

BY LISA SWERLING & RALPH LAZAR

HAROLD'S PLANET

MQP

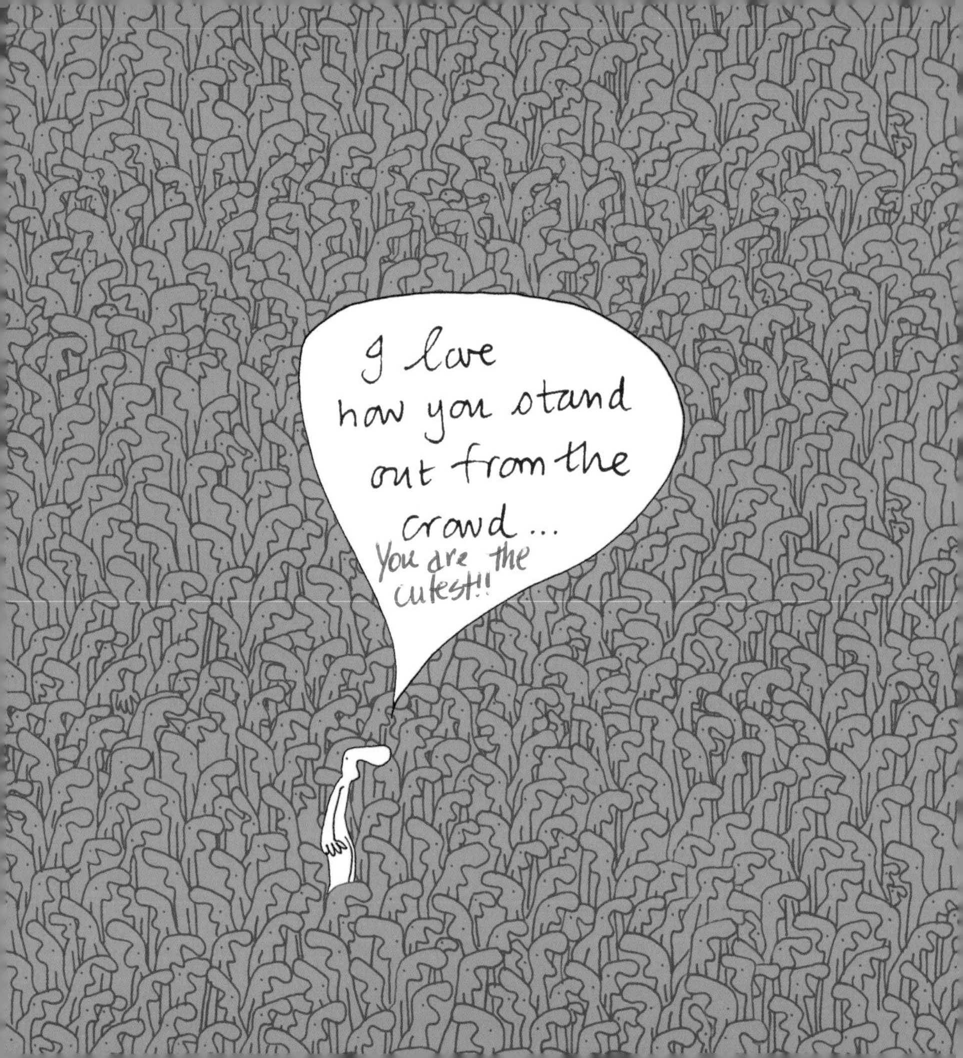
I love how you stand out from the crowd...
You are the cutest!!

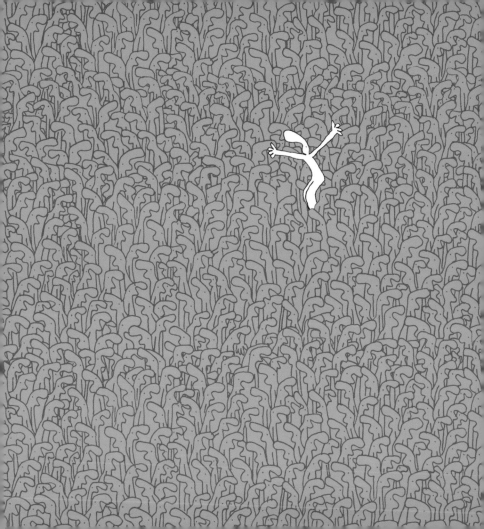

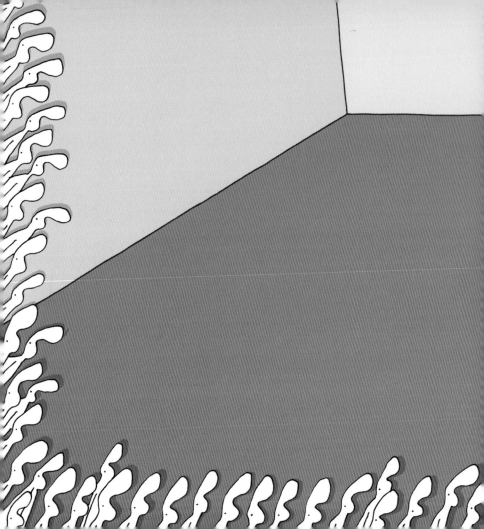

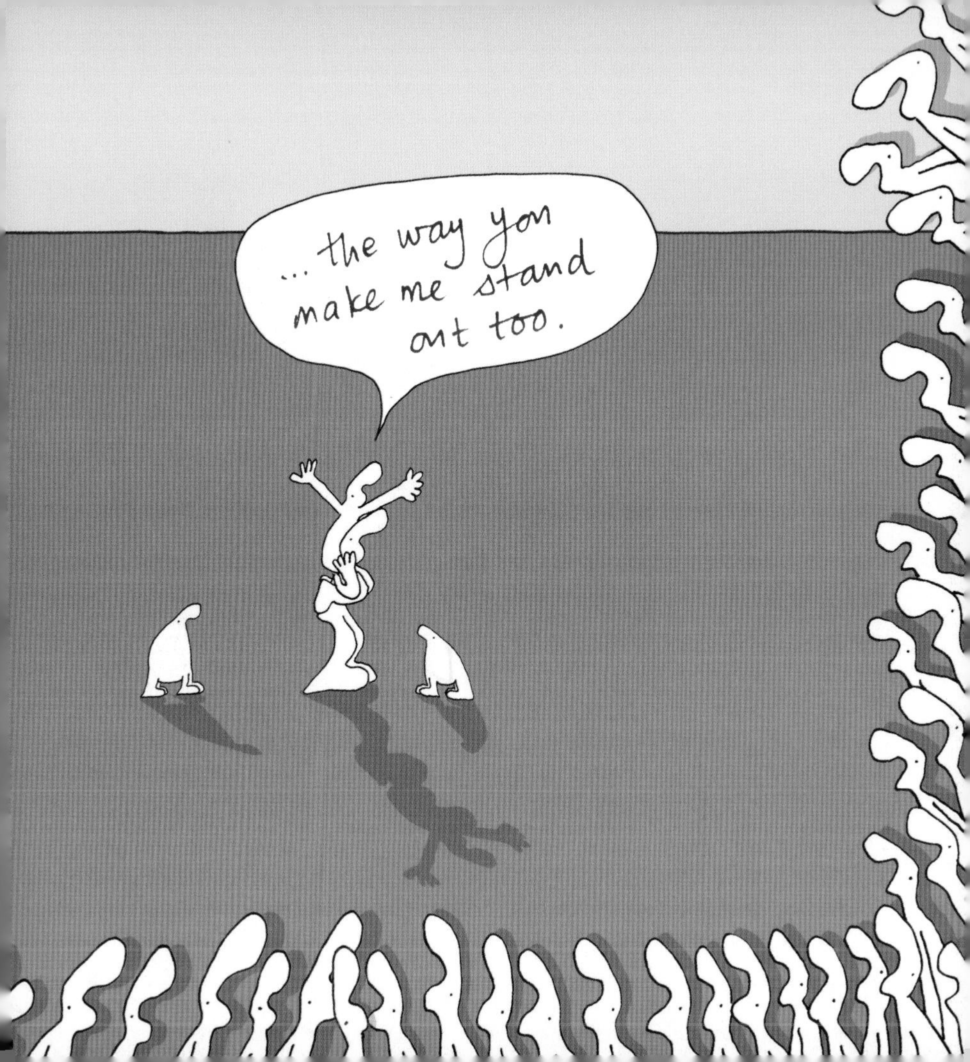

... the way you make me stand out too.

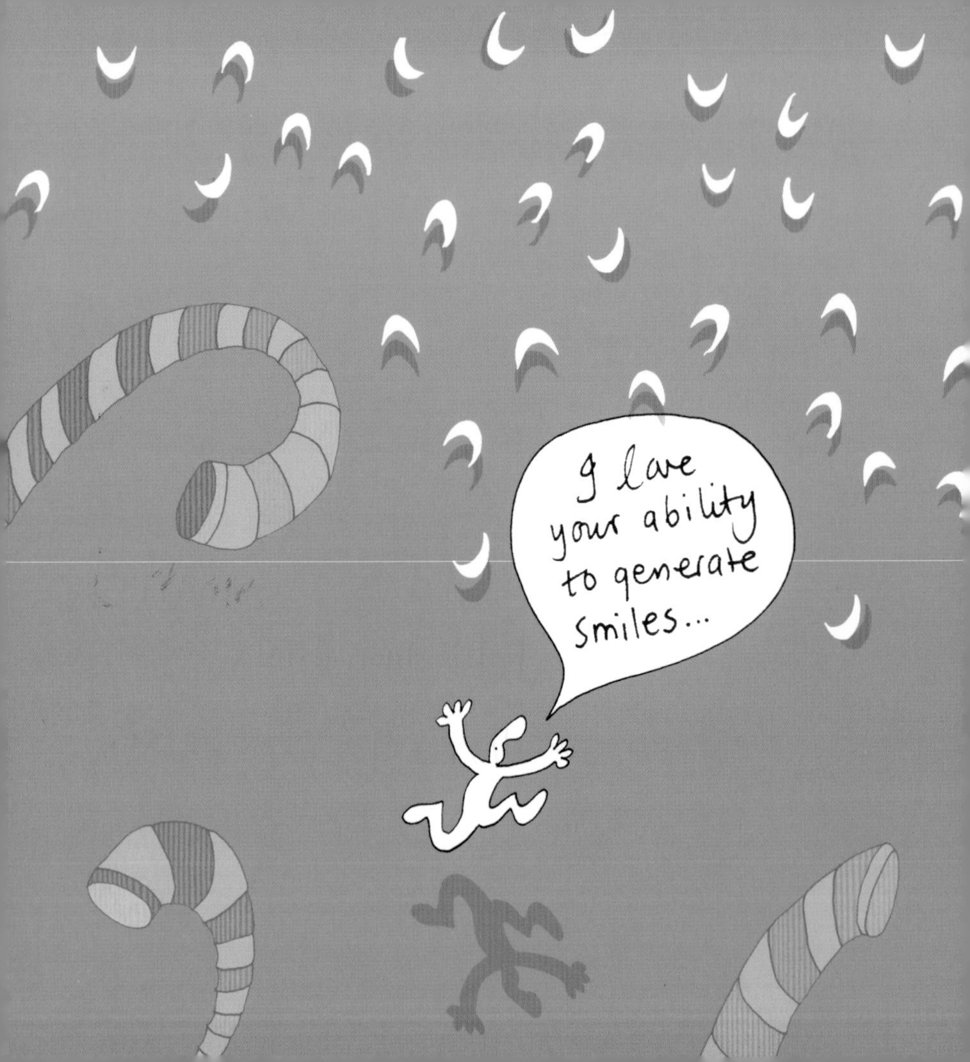
I love your ability to generate smiles...

Lorraine...
Saturday Night Live...
Everything you do...

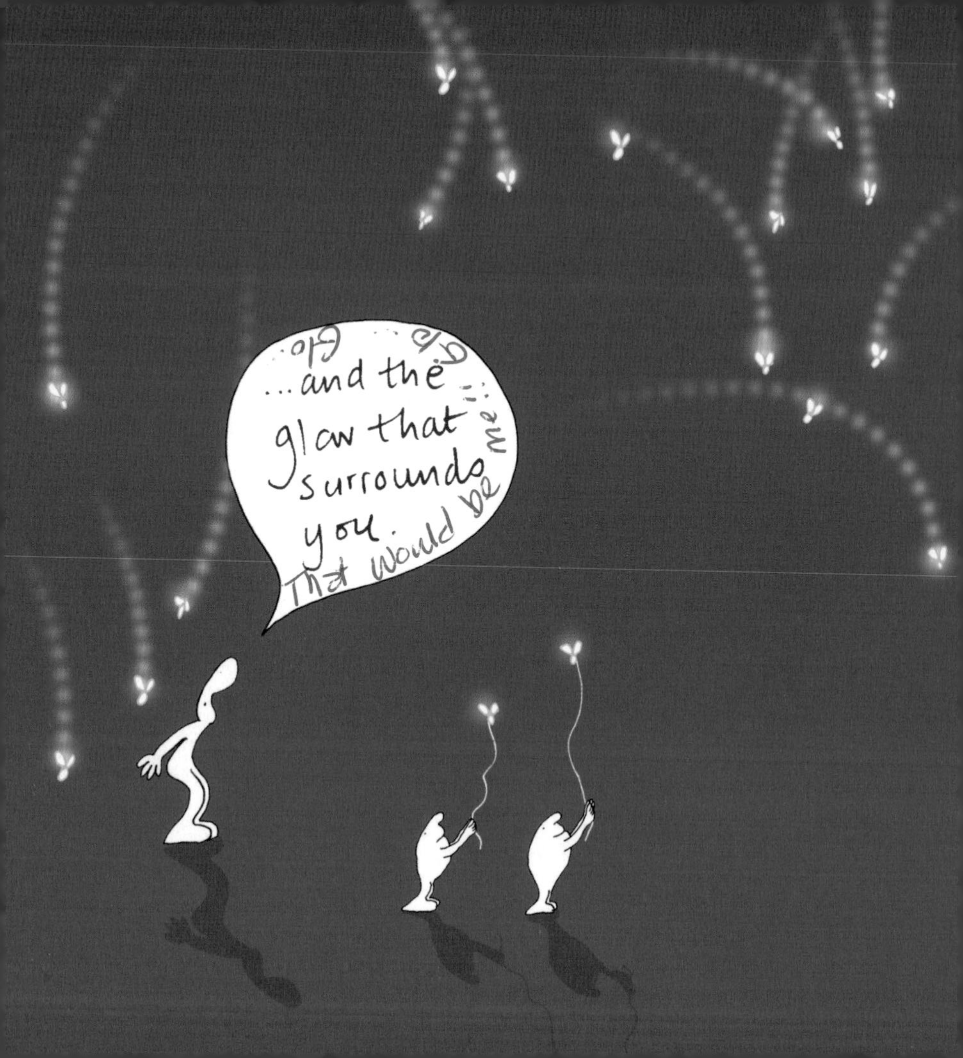
...and the glow that surrounds you.
That would be me!!
Glo... Glo

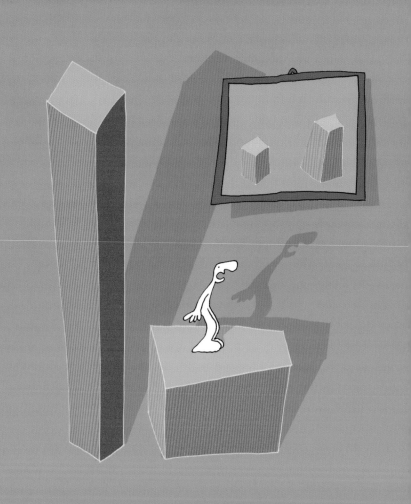

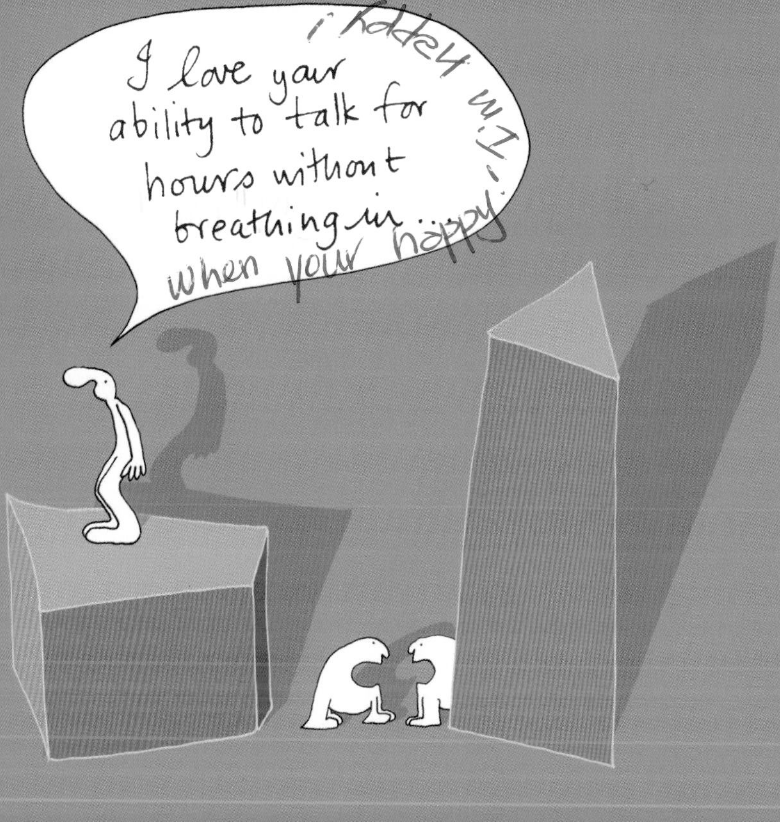
I love your ability to talk for hours without breathing in...

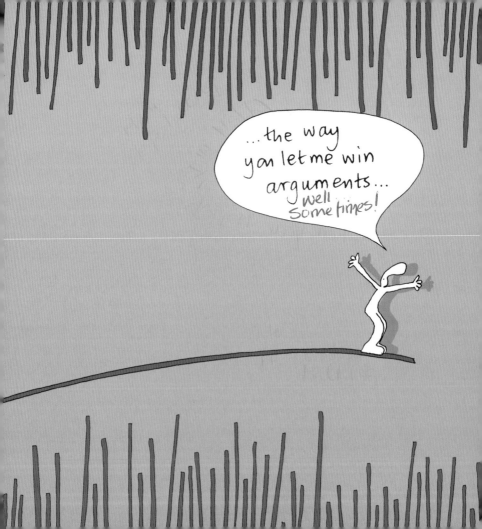

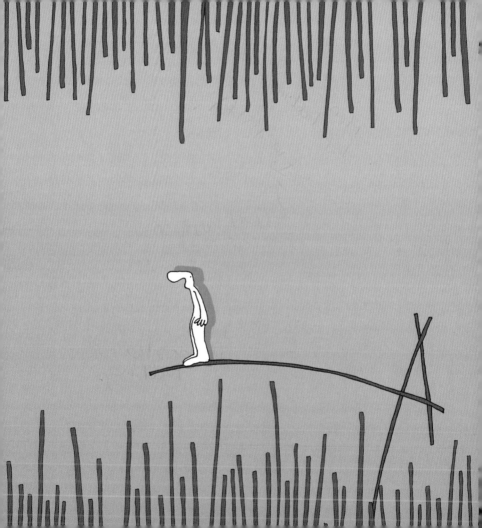

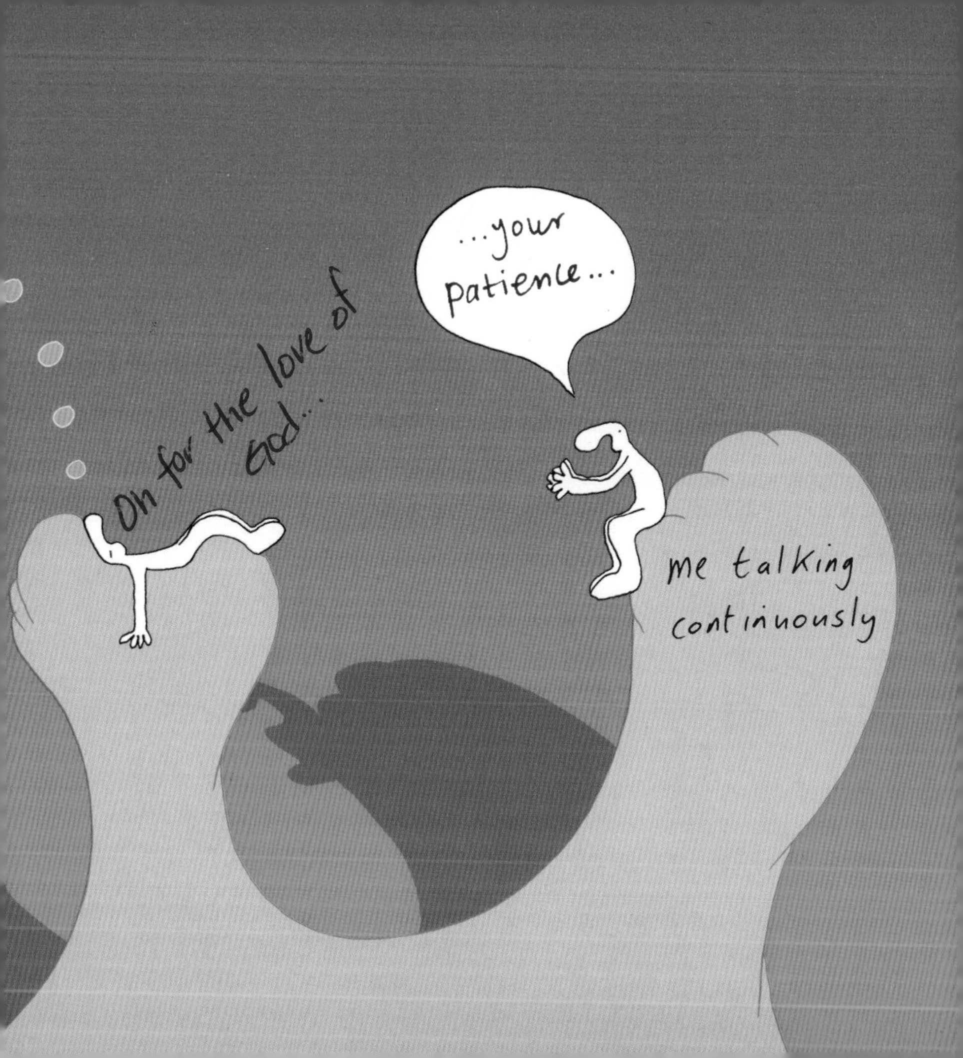
Oh for the love of God...
...your patience...
me talking continuously

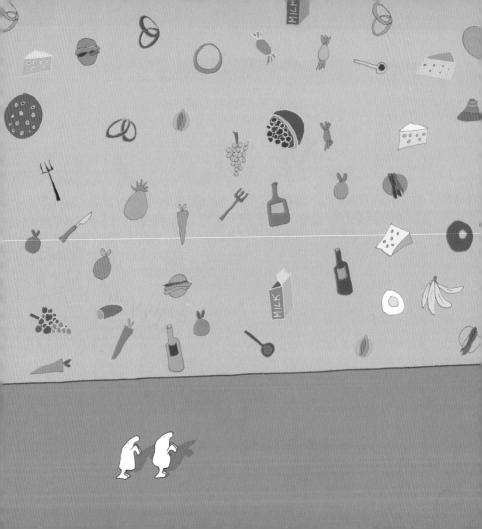

...your knack for finding missing stuff...
Where's Taylor's Bus Pass??

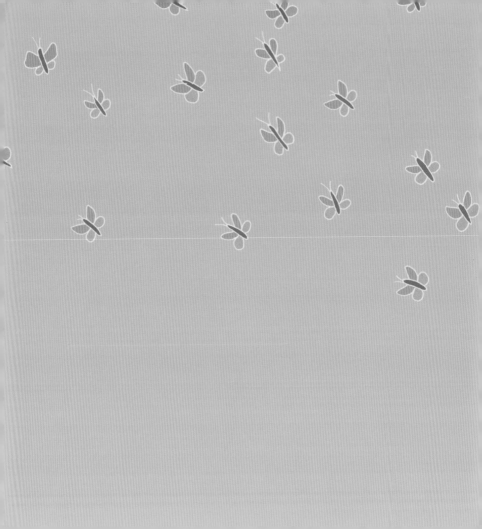

...how I can float on your laughter.
Your Happy I'm Happy!
hee hee
hohohohohohoho
hahahahahaha

BBRRRRBBBRRRRRRRRRRRR

I love how you don't take me for granted... YOU R The Best!
That was the finest boiled egg I've ever had the pleasure to eat, ever.

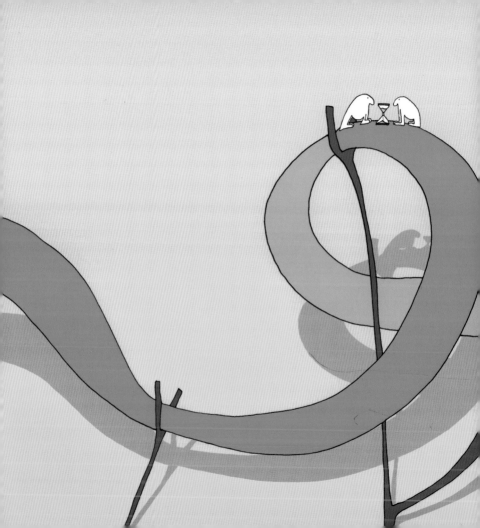

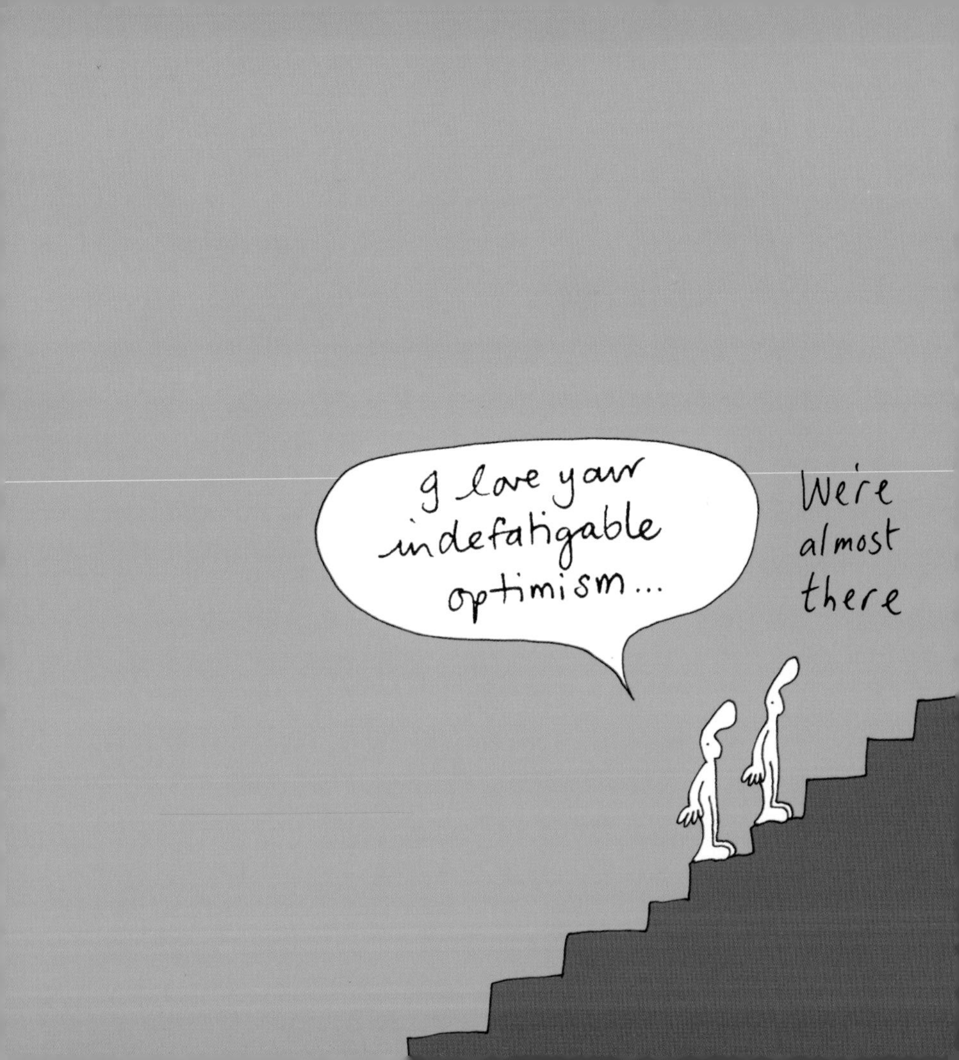
I love your indefatigable optimism...
We're almost there

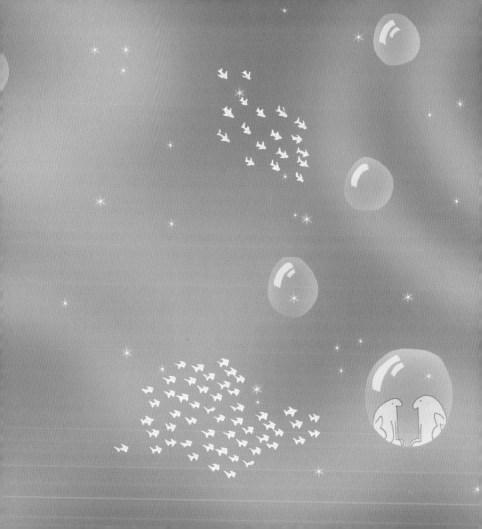

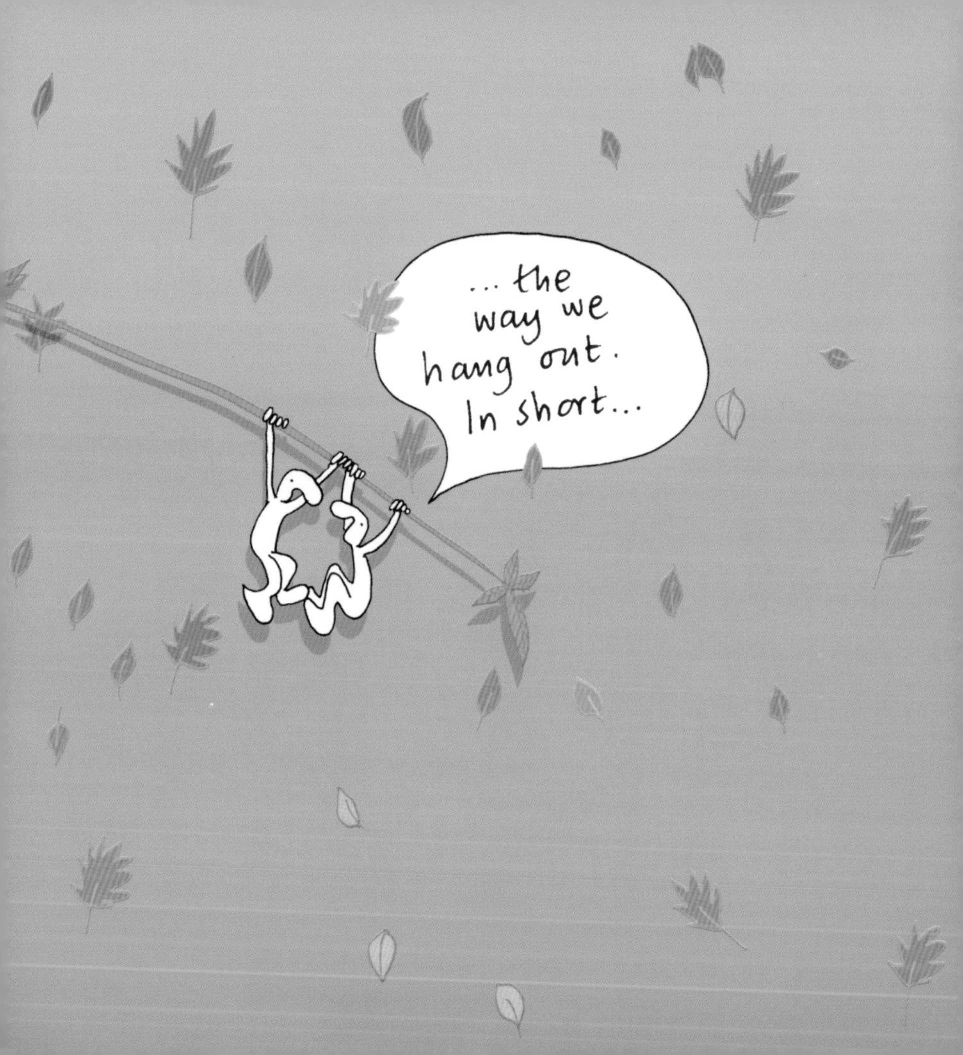
... the way we hang out. In short...

ABOUT THE AUTHORS

Ralph Lazar, Lisa Swerling and their daughter Bea are currently based in the UK. They have recently applied for visas to Harold's Planet, and are expected to move there as soon as the paperwork has been processed.

This book is for B. Rosie

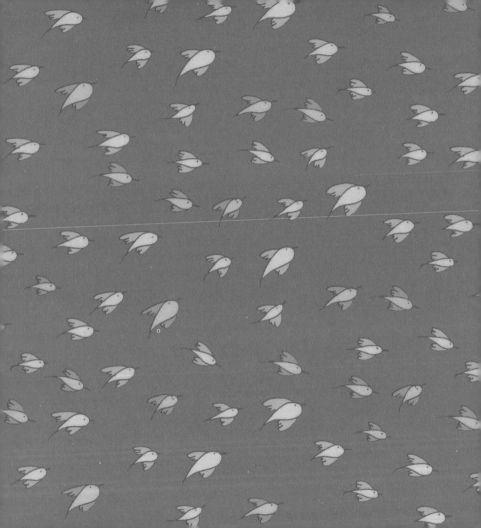